Math Workbook For Kids With Dyscalculia

A resource toolkit book with 100 math activities to help overcome difficulties with numbers

Volume 3

EasyMathGrowth

Introduction

Dyscalculia does not assume that the child does not have the ability to learn mathematics, but rather that a child has a different way of receiving, processing, interpreting mathematical information and therefore, it can and should be corrected with adequate stimulation. Through a specific re-education itinerary that encourages the formation of mental connections, dyscalculia can be overcome.

Dyscalculia must be treated in a very personalized way with each child, making a specific itinerary for each student based on the neuropsychological evaluation that allows knowing what the specific needs of the child are. The intervention by a professional focuses on a cognitive reeducation itinerary with the aim of stimulating or creating a new neural connection responsible for number concepts and number sense.

Ways to help your child with math:

1. Use the exercises to strengthen their number sense. These are basic number exercises such as simple operations, quantities and so on. You will find many of these in this book.

2. Use number games. Using games provides a fun sense that favors stimulation and learning.

3. Work with your child or student basic mathematical concepts such as quantity, proportion (greater, less, much, little ...) and serialization.

4. Lean on visual references that help them understand mathematics (charts, drawings, diagrams ...)

5. Teach your child or student the correspondence between operations and mathematical language (add: union; subtract: remove; multiply: add the same number; divide: distribution)

6. Help them to visualize the problems and to unravel the facts and questions.

7. Train mental math through repeated activities so you will be giving

the child with dyscalculia cognitive strategies for math.

8. It is very important that you always give the child the time they need to learn and create the relevant neural substrate

9. Take care of the emotional well-being of the child. It is key that you offer emotional support to avoid derived problems.

10. Adapt the learning process to each child, at their level, their knowledge, their starting needs, etc.

Table of Contents

Table of Contents

NUMBERS

In this chapter, students will learn to:
- Count to 100, forward and backwards, beginning with

0, 1 or any given number.

- Place value and identify smaller or larger number

-Count in words (one - twenty).

-Skip count by 2's and 3's

Count and Write

Count and write the number of each object in the circle.

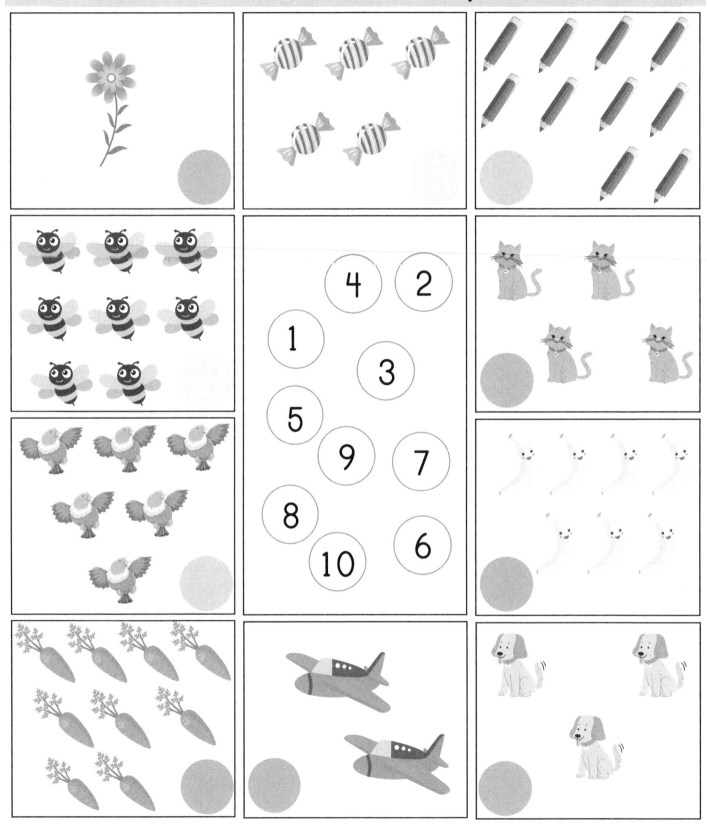

Count and Write

Count and write the number of colored boxes.

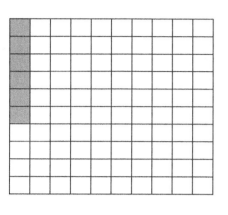 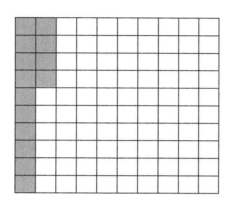 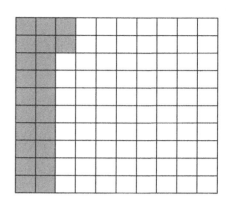

_____ _____ _____

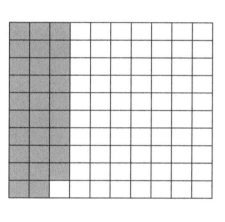 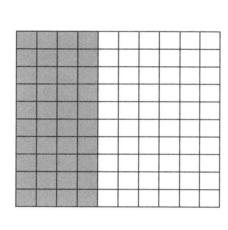 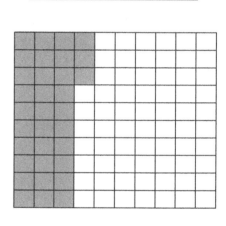

_____ _____ _____

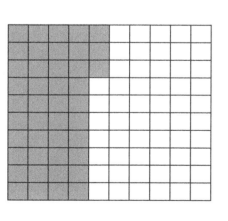 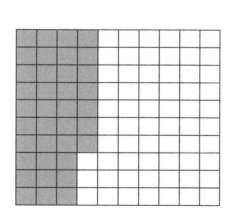 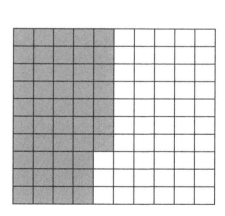

_____ _____ _____

Connect the Dots

Connect the dots by counting from 1 - 50 and color the picture.

Count and Color

Count and color the number of boxes as mentioned.

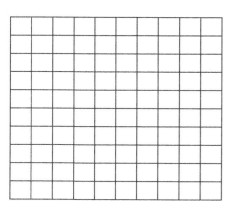

12

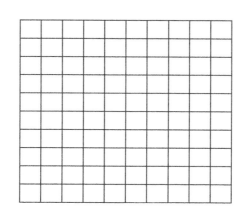

27

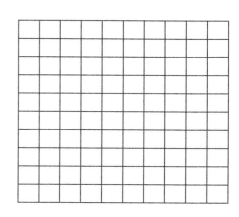

33

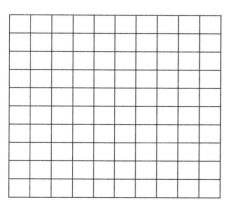

49

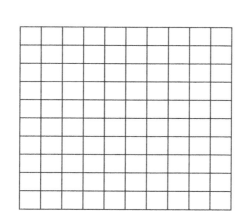

58

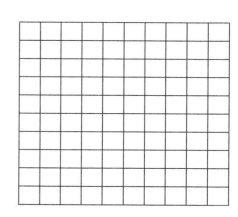

65

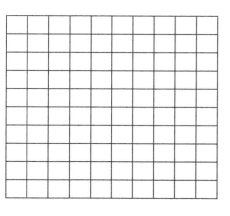

72

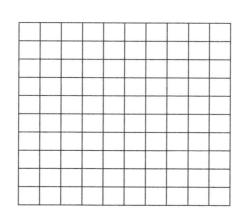

87

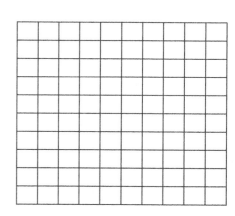

94

Connect the Dots

Connect the dots by counting from 51 - 100 and color the picture.

Before, After, and Between

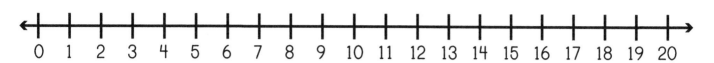

① _____ , 3   ② _____ , 7

③ _____ , 10   ④ _____ , 14

⑤ _____ , 16   ⑥ _____ , 20

Write the number that is just after.

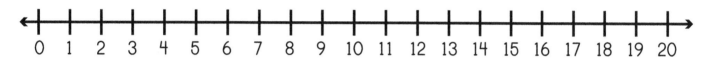

① 2 , _____   ② 5 , _____

③ 8 , _____   ④ 11 , _____

⑤ 15 , _____   ⑥ 18 , _____

Write the number that is in between.

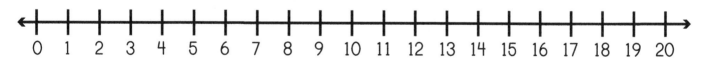

① 4 , _____ , 6   ② 7 , _____ , 9

③ 10 , _____ , 12   ④ 12 , _____ , 14

⑤ 16 , _____ , 18   ⑥ 18 , _____ , 20

Before, After, and Between

Write the number in order from least to greatest.

1.

_____ , _____ , _____
least   between greatest

2.

_____ , _____ , _____
least   between greatest

3.

_____ , _____ , _____
least   between greatest

4.

_____ , _____ , _____
least   between greatest

5.

_____ , _____ , _____
least   between greatest

6.

_____ , _____ , _____
least   between greatest

7.

| 12 | 18 | 15 |

_____ , _____ , _____
least   between greatest

8.

| 28 | 33 | 23 |

_____ , _____ , _____
least   between greatest

9.

| 30 | 43 | 34 |

_____ , _____ , _____
least   between greatest

10.

| 45 | 50 | 41 |

_____ , _____ , _____
least   between greatest

Hundreds Chart

Use the hundreds chart to write the numbers in order.

1	2	3	4	5	6	7	8	9	10
11	12	13	14	15	16	17	18	19	20
21	22	23	24	25	26	27	28	29	30
31	32	33	34	35	36	37	38	39	40
41	42	43	44	45	46	47	48	49	50
51	52	53	54	55	56	57	58	59	60
61	62	63	64	65	66	67	68	69	70
71	72	73	74	75	76	77	78	79	80
81	82	83	84	85	86	87	88	89	90
91	92	93	94	95	96	97	98	99	100

1) 51 , _____ , 53

2) 55 , _____ , 57

3) _____ , 58 , 59

4) _____ , 61 , 62

5) 63 , 64 , _____

6) 64 , 65 , _____

7) 66 , _____ , 68

8) 71 , _____ , 73

9) _____ , 73 , 74

10) _____ , 75 , 76

11) 77 , 78 , _____

12) 79 , 80 , _____

13) 76 , _____ , 78

14) 80 , _____ , 82

15) _____ , 83 , 84

16) _____ , 85 , 86

17) 88 , 89 , _____

18) 93 , 94 , _____

9

Numbers in Words

1. One   (a) 1   (b) 2   (c) 3

2. Three   (a) 2   (b) 3   (c) 4

3. Four   (a) 4   (b) 5   (c) 6

4. Six   (a) 5   (b) 6   (c) 7

5. Nine   (a) 7   (b) 8   (c) 9

Match the numbers to their written words.

12	Eleven
15	Twelve
17	Fourteen
11	Fifteen
20	Sixteen
16	Seventeen
14	Twenty

Ten up to 100

1 ten is _____

2 tens are _____

3 tens are _____

4 tens are _____

5 tens are _____

6 tens are _____

7 tens are _____

8 tens are _____

9 tens are _____

10 tens are _____

Place Value to 100

Tens

Ones

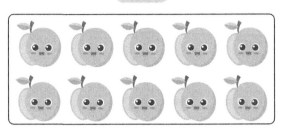 

_____ tens   +   _____ ones   =   _____

Tens

Ones

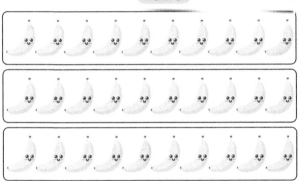 

_____ tens   +   _____ ones   =   _____

Tens

Ones

 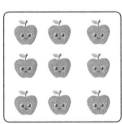

_____ tens   +   _____ ones   =   _____

Expanded Form

Tens  Ones

_____ tens + _____ ones = _____

20 + 2 = _____

Tens  Ones

_____ tens + _____ ones = _____

_____ + _____ = _____

Tens  Ones

_____ tens + _____ ones = _____

_____ + _____ = _____

What number does the abacus show?

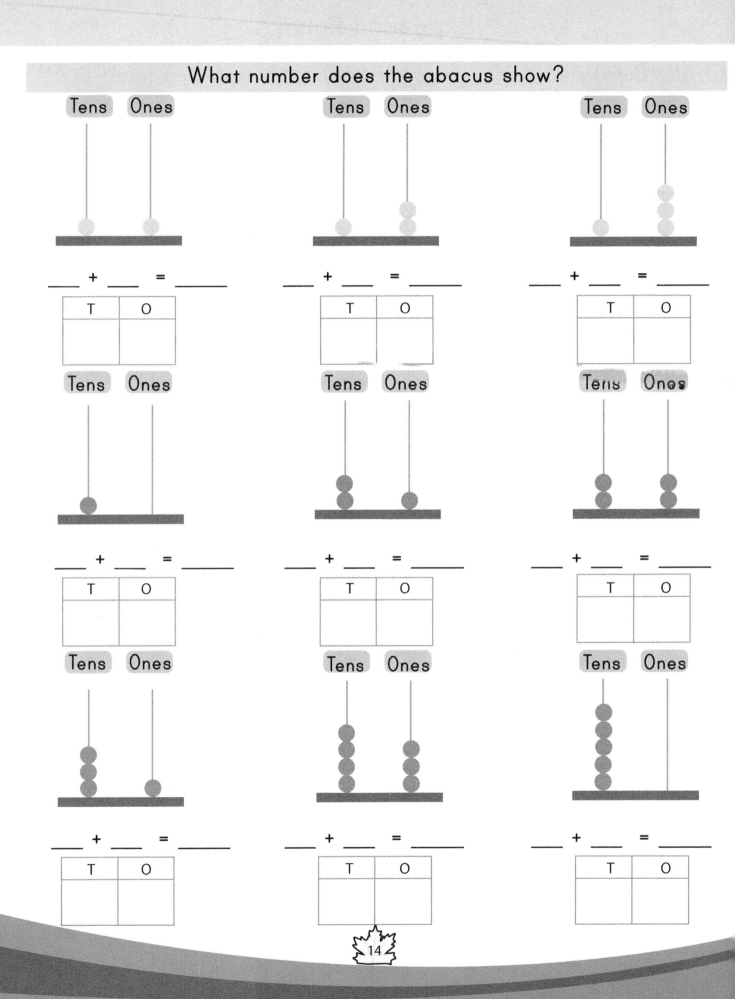

Tens   Ones

___ + ___ = ___

T	O

Tens   Ones

___ + ___ = ___

T	O

Tens   Ones

___ + ___ = ___

T	O

Tens   Ones

___ + ___ = ___

T	O

Tens   Ones

___ + ___ = ___

T	O

Tens   Ones

___ + ___ = ___

T	O

Tens   Ones

___ + ___ = ___

T	O

Tens   Ones

___ + ___ = ___

T	O

Tens   Ones

___ + ___ = ___

T	O

Place Value

Identify and sort the tens and ones in each number.

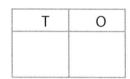 Eleven

T	O

11 is _____ tens and _____ ones

 Twelve

T	O

12 is _____ tens and _____ ones

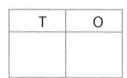 Thriteen

T	O

13 is _____ tens and _____ ones

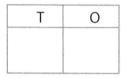 Fourteen

T	O

14 is _____ tens and _____ ones

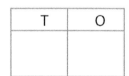 Fitteen

T	O

15 is _____ tens and _____ ones

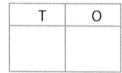 Seventeen

T	O

17 is _____ tens and _____ ones

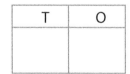 Nineteen

T	O

19 is _____ tens and _____ ones

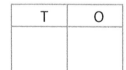 Twenty

T	O

20 is _____ tens and _____ ones

Skip Counting by 2's

Color the boxes by counting by 2's.

1	2	3	4	5	6	7

8

9

10

11

18	17	16	15	14	13	12

19

20

21

22

23	24	25	26	27	28	29

Skip Counting by 3's

Color the boxes by counting by 3's.

1	2	3	4	5	6	7
						8
						9
						10
17	16	15	14	13	12	11
18	19	20	21	22	23	24
						25
						26
						27
34	33	32	31	30	29	28

NUMBER OPERATIONS

In this chapter, students will learn to:

- Solve additions using one and two digit numbers, with or without carry, and addition word problems

- Solve subtractions with one and two digit numbers, with or without borrowing, and subtraction word problems

- Add and subtract on a number line and use the hundreds chart

-Use the 2 and 3 times tables,

- Solve mixed problems

Adding on a Number Line

Hop on the number line and count.

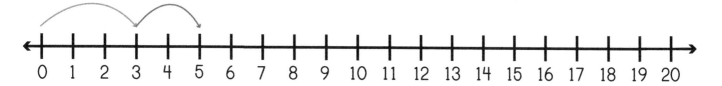

_____ + _____ = _____

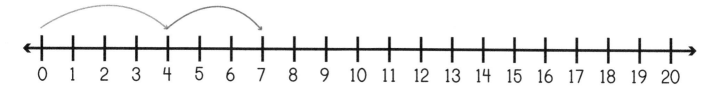

_____ + _____ = _____

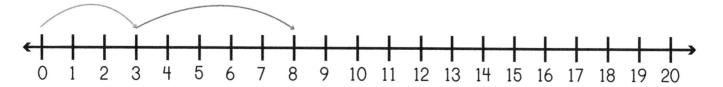

_____ + _____ = _____

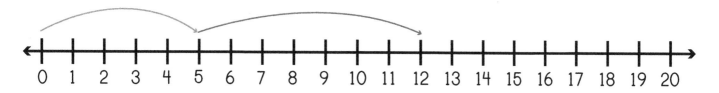

_____ + _____ = _____

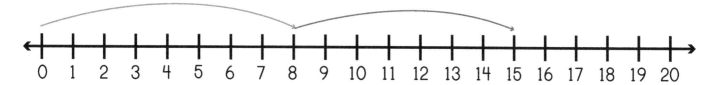

_____ + _____ = _____

Number Bonds of 2 and 3

Complete the number bonds to show all of the different ways to get 2.

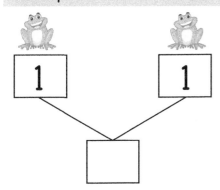

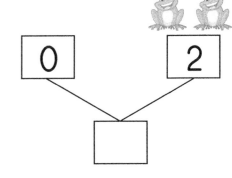

Complete the number bonds to show all of the different ways to get 3.

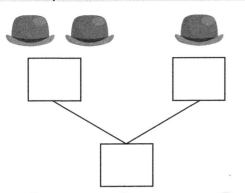

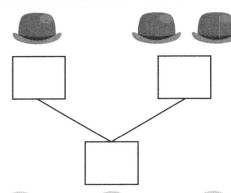

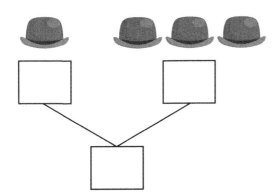

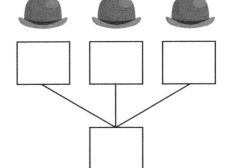

Adding Zero

 + 0

 + 0

 + 0

🥕🥕🥕🥕 + 0

0 more than 5 is

0 more than 6 is

0 more than 7 is

There are 2 🦋 in the garden. 0 more join in. How many 🦋 are there now?

$$
\begin{array}{r}
2 \quad \text{🦋🦋} \\
+\ 0 \\
\hline

\end{array}
$$

Number Bonds of 4

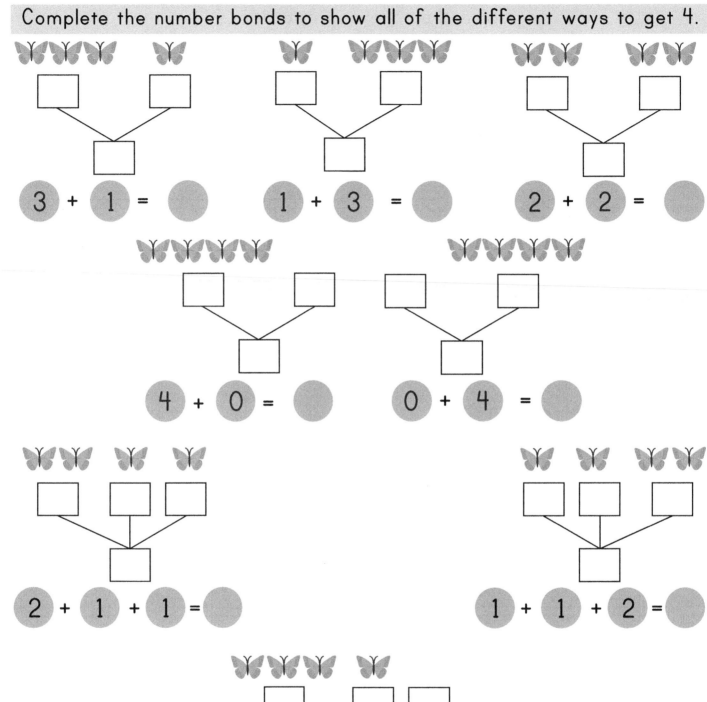

3 + 1 = ⬤

1 + 3 = ⬤

2 + 2 = ⬤

4 + 0 = ⬤

0 + 4 = ⬤

2 + 1 + 1 = ⬤

1 + 1 + 2 = ⬤

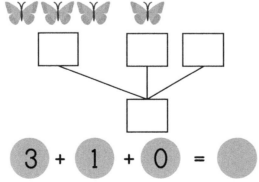

3 + 1 + 0 = ⬤

Adding One

 + 1

 + 1

 + 1

 + 1

1 more than 5 is

1 more than 6 is

1 more than 7 is

Meena sold 3 . Jane sold 1 more. How many do they sell in all?

$$\begin{array}{r} 3 \\ + 1 \\ \hline \end{array}$$

Number Bonds Of 5

Complete the number bonds to show all of the different ways to get 5.

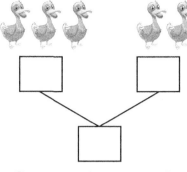

3 + 2 = ○

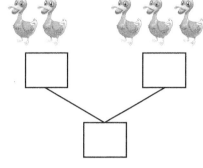

2 + 3 = ○

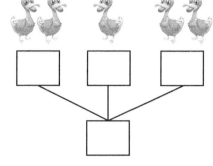

2 + 1 + 2 = ○

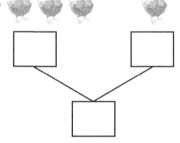

4 + 1 = ○

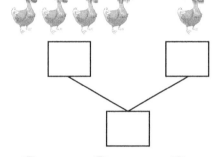

1 + 4 = ○

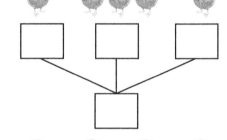

1 + 3 + 1 = ○

Write all of the different ways to get 5.

2+3

= 5

Adding Two

 + 2

 + 2

 + 2

 + 2

2 more than 5 is

2 more than 6 is

2 more than 7 is

Elis has 3 pairs of shoes . She buys 2 more. How many pairs of shoes are their in total?

$$3$$
$$+\ 2$$

Number Bonds of 6

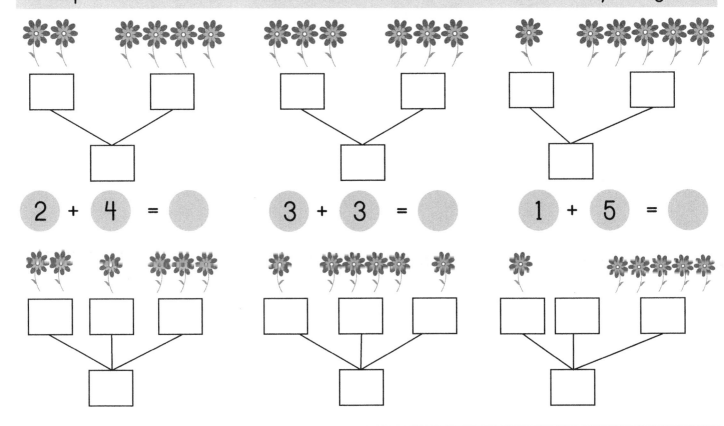

2 + 4 = ⬤   3 + 3 = ⬤   1 + 5 = ⬤

Write all of the different ways to get 6.

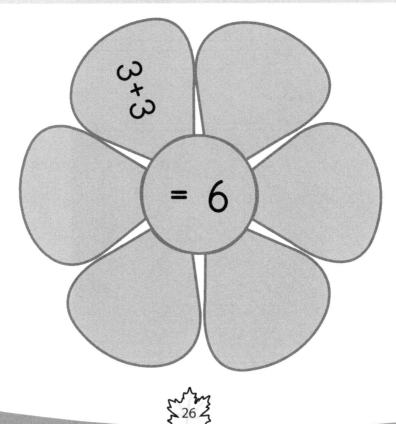

3+3 = 6

Adding Three

 + 3

 + 3

 + 3

 + 3

3 more than 5 is

3 more than 6 is

3 more than 7 is

Jack has three . He gets 3 more. How many are their in total?

$$\begin{array}{r} 3 \\ + \ 3 \\ \hline \\ \hline \end{array}$$

Number Bonds of 7

Complete the number bonds to show all of the different ways to get 7.

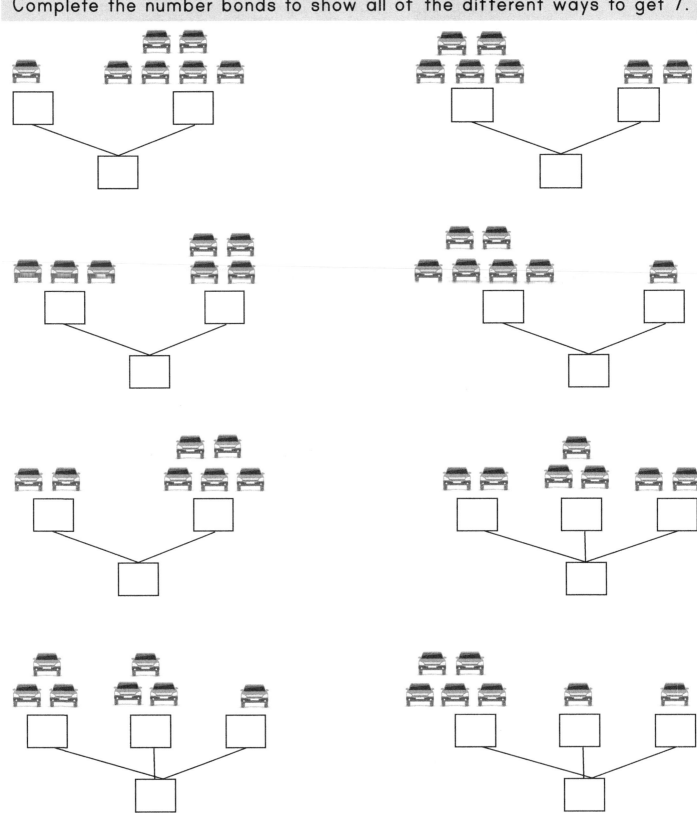

Number Bonds of 7

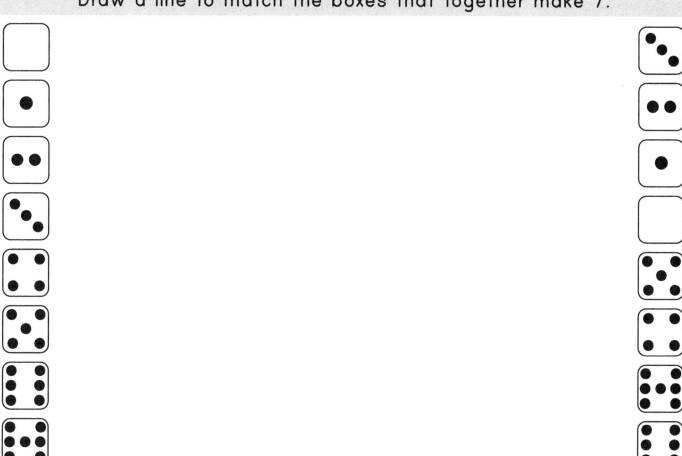

Write all of the different ways to get 7.

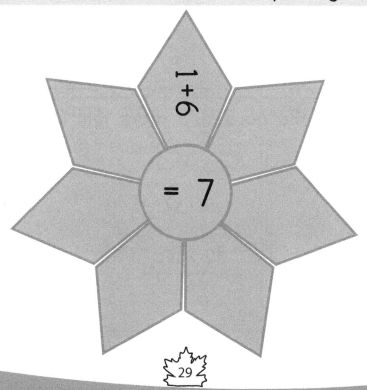

Adding Four

🏀 + 4

👟👟 + 4

🦆🦆🦆 + 4

🥕🥕🥕🥕 + 4

4 more than 5 is

4 more than 6 is

4 more than 7 is

There are 3 🐦 in the garden. 4 more join in. How many 🐦 are there now?

$$
\begin{array}{r}
3 \\
+ \ 4 \\
\hline
\\
\hline
\end{array}
$$

Number Bonds of 8

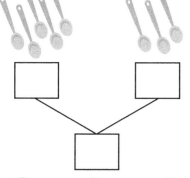

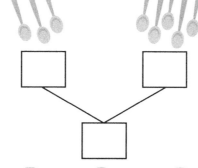

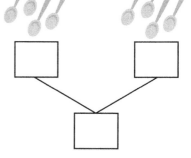

5 + 3 = ◯   3 + 5 = ◯   4 + 4 = ◯

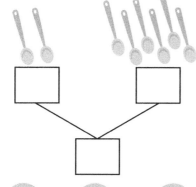

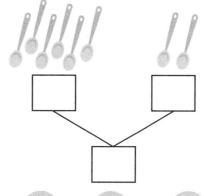

2 + 6 = ◯   6 + 2 = ◯

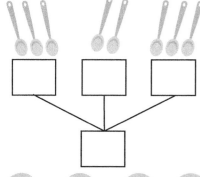

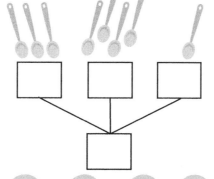

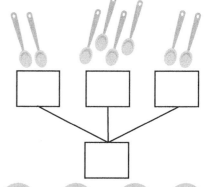

3 + 2 + 3 = ◯   3 + 4 + 1 = ◯   2 + 4 + 2 = ◯

31

Number Bonds of 8

Color the boxes that together make 8.

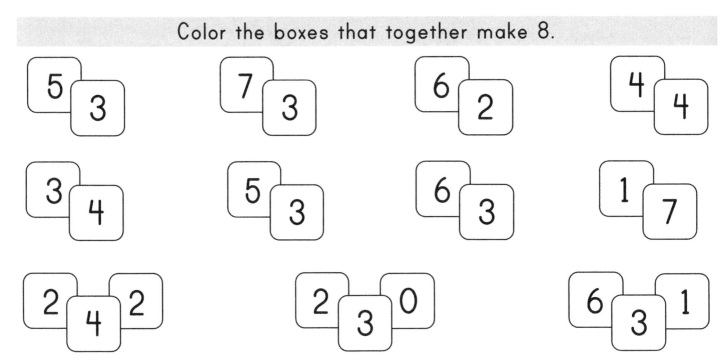

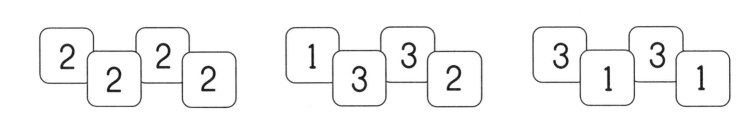

32

Adding Five

⊕ + 5	
👟👟 + 5	
🦆🦆🦆 + 5	
🥕🥕🥕🥕 + 5	
5 more than 5 is	
5 more than 6 is	
5 more than 7 is	

There are 4 on the grass. 5 more join in. How many  are there now?

$$
\begin{array}{r}
4 \\
+\ 5 \\
\hline
\\
\hline
\end{array}
$$

Doubles

Draw the shapes and find the doubles.

Draw two more circles and count all of them.

●● + [ ] = _____

Draw three more squares and count all of them.

■■■ + [ ] = _____

Draw four more triangles and count all of them.

▲▲▲▲ + [ ] = _____

Draw five more stars and count all of them.

★★★★★ + [ ] = _____

Draw six more circles and count all of them.

●●●●●● + [ ] = _____

Draw seven more squares and count all of them..

■■■■■■■ + [ ] = _____

Draw eight more triangles and count all of them.

▲▲▲▲▲▲▲▲ + [ ] = _____

Draw nine more stars and count all of them.

★★★★★★★★★ + [ ] = _____

Draw ten more rectangles and count all of them.

▮▮▮▮▮▮▮▮▮▮ + [ ] = _____

Number Bonds of 9

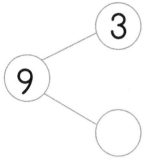

☐ + ☐ = ☐

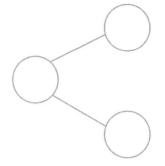

☐ + ☐ = ☐

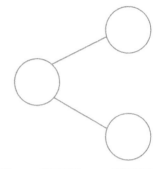

☐ + ☐ = ☐

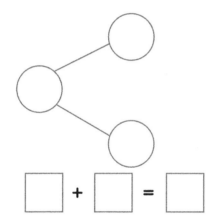

☐ + ☐ = ☐

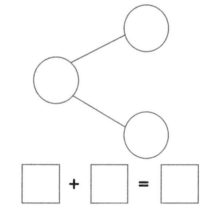

☐ + ☐ = ☐

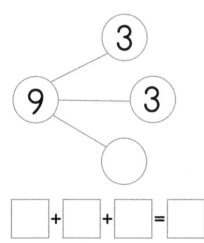

☐ + ☐ + ☐ = ☐

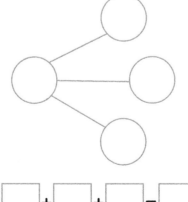

☐ + ☐ + ☐ = ☐

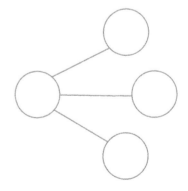

☐ + ☐ + ☐ = ☐

Number Bonds of 9

Write all of the different ways to get 9.

Color the boxes that together make 9.

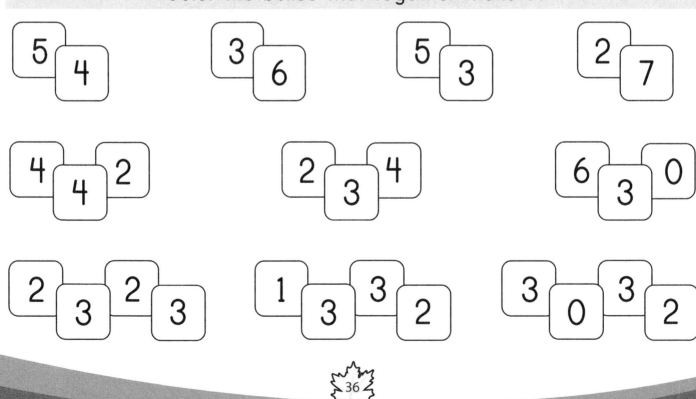

36

Adding Six

Solve the following operations.

 + 6

 + 6

 + 6

6 more than 4 is

6 more than 5 is

What do we get by adding 6 and 6?

What do we get by adding 6 and 7?

Leena buys 3 toys. She gets 6 more. How many toys does she have altogether?

+
___

___

Number Bonds of 10

Make the number bonds that show all of the different ways to get 10.

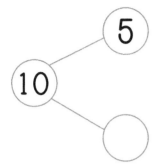

◻ + ◻ = ◻

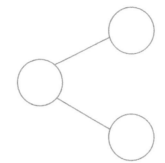

◻ + ◻ = ◻

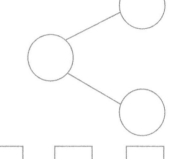

◻ + ◻ = ◻

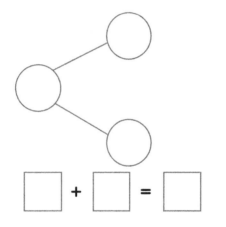

◻ + ◻ = ◻

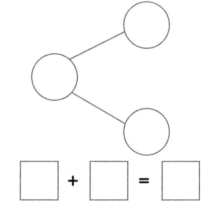

◻ + ◻ = ◻

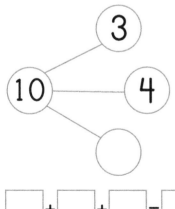

◻ + ◻ + ◻ = ◻

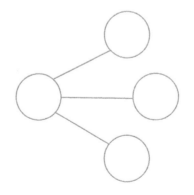

◻ + ◻ + ◻ = ◻

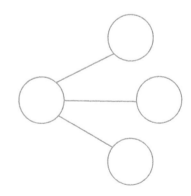

◻ + ◻ + ◻ = ◻

38

Number Bonds of 10

Draw a line to match the boxes that together make 10.

Color the boxes that together make 10.

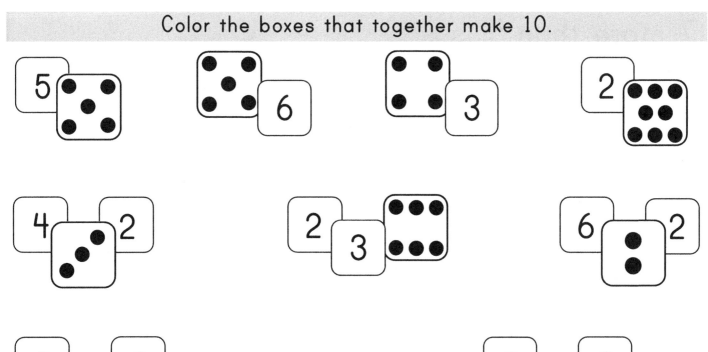

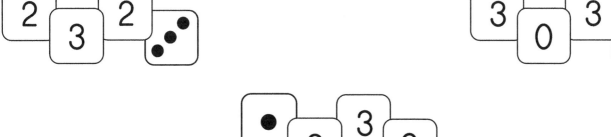

39

Adding Seven

![bug] + 7	
![apples] + 7	
![candies] + 7	
7 more than 4 is	
7 more than 5 is	
what do we get by adding 7 and 6?	
What do we get by adding 7 and 7?	

There are 5 milk cans on the table. 7 more have been placed. How many milk cans are there altogether?

$$+$$

$$\overline{\qquad\qquad}$$

$$\overline{\qquad\qquad}$$

Number Sentences and Number Bonds

Look at pictures and write number sentences and number bonds.

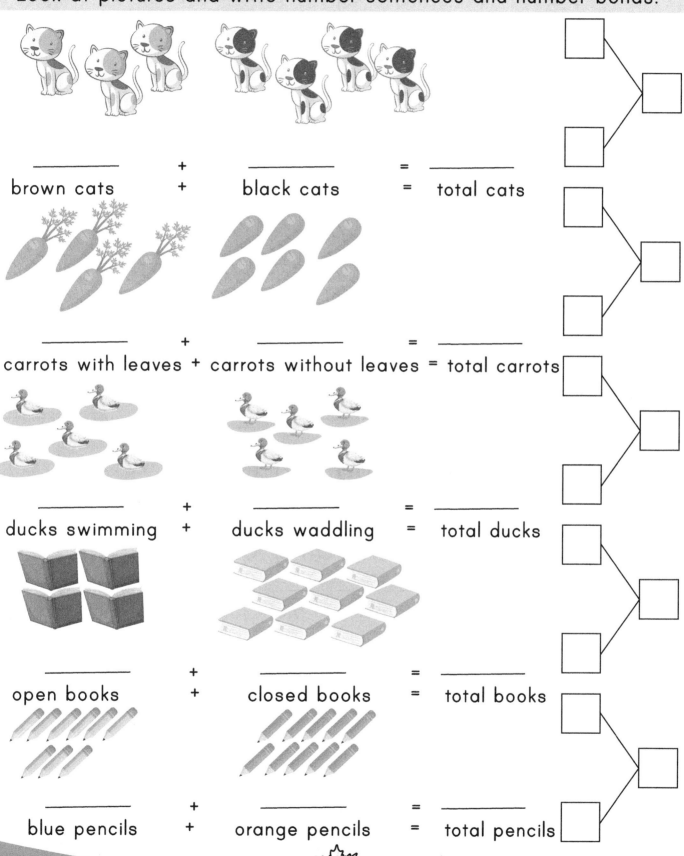

_____ + _____ = _____
brown cats + black cats = total cats

_____ + _____ = _____
carrots with leaves + carrots without leaves = total carrots

_____ + _____ = _____
ducks swimming + ducks waddling = total ducks

_____ + _____ = _____
open books + closed books = total books

_____ + _____ = _____
blue pencils + orange pencils = total pencils

Adding Eight

+ 8	
+ 8	
+ 8	

8 more than 4 is	
8 more than 5 is	
What do we get by adding 8 and 6?	
What do we get by adding 8 and 7?	

There are 5 players on the ground. 8 more join in. How many players are there altogether?

$$+ \underline{\qquad}$$

$$\underline{\qquad}$$

Addition Word Problems

1. There are 4 🐱s on the street. 2 🐱s join in. How many 🐱s are there altogether?

$$\begin{array}{r} 4 \\ + 2 \\ \hline \end{array}$$

2. Jane has 6 🍪 .She got 3 more. How many 🍪 does she have altogether?

$$\begin{array}{r} 6 \\ + 3 \\ \hline \end{array}$$

3. Austin has 7 📘 .Ashley has 4 📘 . How many 📘 do they have altogether?

$$\begin{array}{r} 7 \\ + 4 \\ \hline \end{array}$$

4. There are 9 🐦 on tree branch. 5 🐦 join in. How many 🐦 are there altogether.

$$\begin{array}{r} 9 \\ + 5 \\ \hline \end{array}$$

Adding Nine

Solve the following operations.

🐛 + 9

🍎🍎 + 9

🍬🍬🍬 + 9

9 more than 4 is

9 more than 5 is

What do we get by adding 9 and 6?

What do we get by adding 9 and 7?

Sila makes 7 dresses. Aina makes 9 dresses. How many dresses do they make altogether?

+
_____

_____

One-digit Addition

(1)
$$\begin{array}{r} 5 \\ + 3 \\ \hline \end{array}$$

(2)
$$\begin{array}{r} 2 \\ + 7 \\ \hline \end{array}$$

(3)
$$\begin{array}{r} 1 \\ + 3 \\ \hline \end{array}$$

(4)
$$\begin{array}{r} 8 \\ + 1 \\ \hline \end{array}$$

(5)
$$\begin{array}{r} 4 \\ + 2 \\ \hline \end{array}$$

(6)
$$\begin{array}{r} 4 \\ + 4 \\ \hline \end{array}$$

(7)
$$\begin{array}{r} 6 \\ + 3 \\ \hline \end{array}$$

(8)
$$\begin{array}{r} 7 \\ + 2 \\ \hline \end{array}$$

(9)
$$\begin{array}{r} 3 \\ + 4 \\ \hline \end{array}$$

(10)
$$\begin{array}{r} 3 \\ + 6 \\ \hline \end{array}$$

(11)
$$\begin{array}{r} 5 \\ + 4 \\ \hline \end{array}$$

(12)
$$\begin{array}{r} 6 \\ + 2 \\ \hline \end{array}$$

(13)
$$\begin{array}{r} 8 \\ + 2 \\ \hline \end{array}$$

(14)
$$\begin{array}{r} 6 \\ + 4 \\ \hline \end{array}$$

(15)
$$\begin{array}{r} 3 \\ + 8 \\ \hline \end{array}$$

Adding Ten

Solve the following operations.

+ 10

+ 10

+ 10

10 more than 4 is

10 more than 5 is

What do we get by adding 10 and 6?

What do we get by adding 10 and 7?

Bia has 8 coins. Anderson has 10 coins. How many coins do they have altogether?

$$+$$

Two-Digit Addition

Remember to add the ones first and then the tens.

	Tens	Ones
(1)	1	2
+		3

	Tens	Ones
(2)	1	2
+		7

	Tens	Ones
(3)	1	4
+		3

	Tens	Ones
(4)	1	4
+		1

	Tens	Ones
(5)	1	0
+		2

	Tens	Ones
(6)	1	4
+		4

	Tens	Ones
(7)	1	6
+		3

	Tens	Ones
(8)	1	7
+		2

	Tens	Ones
(9)	1	3
+		4

	Tens	Ones
(10)	1	3
+		6

	Tens	Ones
(11)	1	5
+		4

	Tens	Ones
(12)	1	6
+		2

	Tens	Ones
(13)	2	7
+		2

	Tens	Ones
(14)	2	5
+		4

	Tens	Ones
(15)	2	1
+		6

Color by Addition

Add the numbers and color each balloon using the color code.

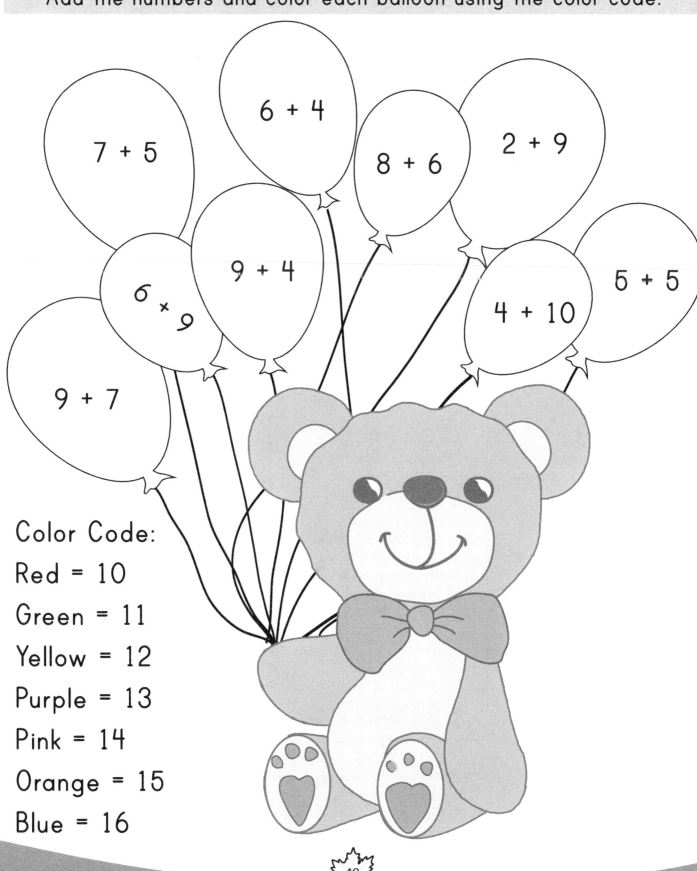

7 + 5

6 + 4

8 + 6

2 + 9

6 + 9

9 + 4

4 + 10

5 + 5

9 + 7

Color Code:

Red = 10

Green = 11

Yellow = 12

Purple = 13

Pink = 14

Orange = 15

Blue = 16

Two-digit Addition

Remember to add the ones first and then the tens.

1)
Tens	Ones
1	5
+ 1	3

2)
Tens	Ones
1	2
+ 1	7

3)
Tens	Ones
2	1
+ 1	3

4)
Tens	Ones
1	8
+ 1	1

5)
Tens	Ones
1	0
+ 2	0

6)
Tens	Ones
1	3
+ 1	4

7)
Tens	Ones
1	6
+ 2	3

8)
Tens	Ones
1	7
+ 2	2

9)
Tens	Ones
1	3
+ 2	4

10)
Tens	Ones
1	3
+ 1	6

11)
Tens	Ones
2	4
+ 1	2

12)
Tens	Ones
1	4
+ 2	5

13)
Tens	Ones
2	7
+ 2	2

14)
Tens	Ones
2	5
+ 2	4

15)
Tens	Ones
2	3
+ 2	6

Two-digit Addition (With Carry)

Remember to add the ones first and then the tens.

1) | Tens | Ones |
|---|---|
| 1 | 6 |
| + 1 | 5 |

2) | Tens | Ones |
|---|---|
| 1 | 4 |
| + 1 | 7 |

3) | Tens | Ones |
|---|---|
| 2 | 7 |
| + 1 | 3 |

4) | Tens | Ones |
|---|---|
| 1 | 8 |
| + 1 | 3 |

5) | Tens | Ones |
|---|---|
| 1 | 9 |
| + 2 | 1 |

6) | Tens | Ones |
|---|---|
| 1 | 6 |
| + 1 | 4 |

7) | Tens | Ones |
|---|---|
| 1 | 7 |
| + 2 | 3 |

8) | Tens | Ones |
|---|---|
| 1 | 7 |
| + 2 | 4 |

9) | Tens | Ones |
|---|---|
| 1 | 5 |
| + 2 | 5 |

10) | Tens | Ones |
|---|---|
| 1 | 6 |
| + 1 | 7 |

11) | Tens | Ones |
|---|---|
| 2 | 7 |
| + 1 | 5 |

12) | Tens | Ones |
|---|---|
| 1 | 6 |
| + 2 | 5 |

Commutative Addition

Write an expression that matches the group on each side. If the group has the same number of objects, write the equal sign between the expressions.

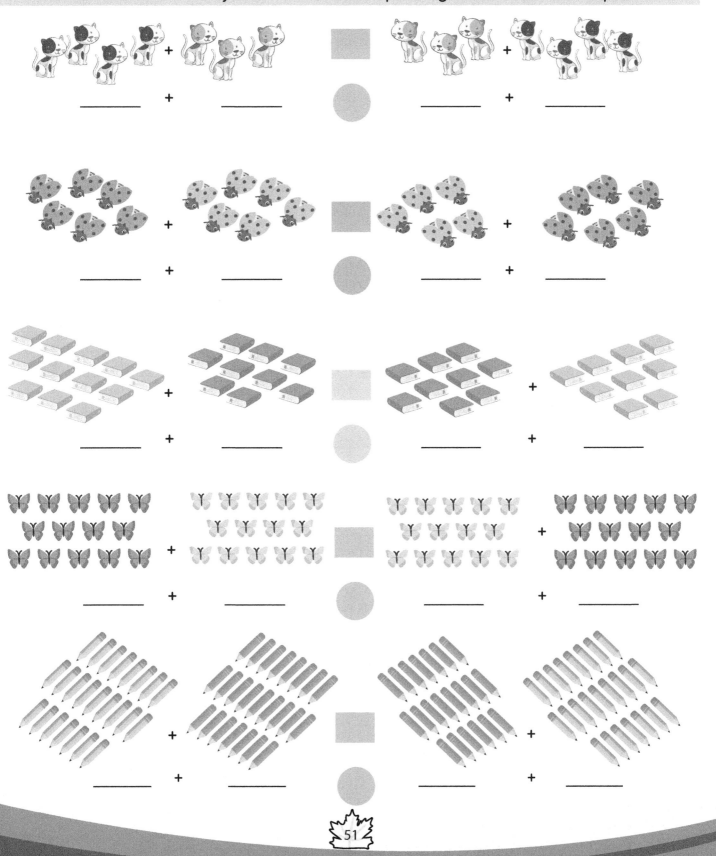

Balance the Equation

Find two ways to make each number sentence true.

| 3 (+) 2 | = | 1 (+) ☐ |
| | | 2 (+) ☐ |

| 4 (+) 3 | = | 2 (+) ☐ |
| | | 5 (+) ☐ |

| 2 (+) 4 | = | 1 (I) ☐ |
| | | 3 (+) ☐ |

| 4 (+) 1 | = | 2 (+) ☐ |
| | | 3 (+) ☐ |

| 7 (+) 2 | = | 5 (+) ☐ |
| | | 3 (+) ☐ |

| 5 (+) 2 | = | 4 (+) ☐ |
| | | 6 (+) ☐ |

| 6 (+) 4 | = | 5 (+) ☐ |
| | | 3 (+) ☐ |

Subtracting on a Number Line

Hop backwards on the number line to count back.

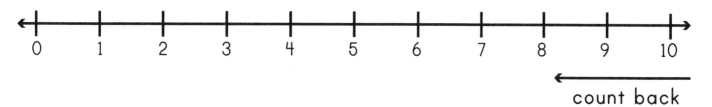

count back

1. $2 - 1 =$ _____

2. $3 - 1 =$ _____

3. $4 - 2 =$ _____

4. $6 - 3 =$ _____

5. $5 - 2 =$ _____

6. $7 - 1 =$ _____

7. $8 - 4 =$ _____

8. $8 - 2 =$ _____

9. $9 - 2 =$ _____

10. $10 - 4 =$ _____

11. $6 - 2 =$ _____

12. $7 - 4 =$ _____

13. $4 - 2 =$ _____

14. $5 - 1 =$ _____

15. $6 - 4 =$ _____

16. $7 - 3 =$ _____

17. $8 - 3 =$ _____

18. $9 - 4 =$ _____

19. $10 - 5 =$ _____

Subtracting Zero

Solve the following operations.

 - 0

 - 0

 - 0

 - 0

0 less than 5 is

0 less than 6 is

0 less than 7 is

There are 3 on a plant. 0 have fallen off. How many are there left?

$$\begin{array}{r} 3 \\ -\ 0 \\ \hline \\ \hline \end{array}$$

Subtracting One

Solve the following operations.

 - 1

 - 1

 - 1

 - 1

1 less than 5 is

1 less than 6 is

1 less than 7 is

There are 2 in the garden. 1 flew away. How many are there left?

2

- 1

___

Subtracting Two

 - 2

 - 2

 - 2

 - 2

2 less than 6 is

2 less than 7 is

2 less than 8 is

Meena sells 3 . Jane sells 2. What is the difference?

$$\begin{array}{r} 3 \\ -\ 2 \\ \hline \end{array}$$

Subtracting Three

 - 3

 - 3

 - 3

 - 3

3 less than 7 is

3 less than 8 is

3 less than 9 is

Elis has 4 pairs of . She gives 3 of them away. How many pairs  does she have left?

$$\begin{array}{r} 4 \\ -\ 3 \\ \hline \\ \hline \end{array}$$

Subtracting Four

 - 4

 - 4

 - 4

 - 4

4 less than 8 is

4 less than 9 is

4 less than 10 is

Jack has 6 . He ate 4 of them. How many does he have left?

$$\begin{array}{r} 6 \\ -\ 4 \\ \hline \\ \hline \end{array}$$

Subtracting Five

 – 5

 – 5

 – 5

 – 5

5 less than 9 is

5 less than 10 is

5 less than 11 is

There are 9 in the garden. 5 flew away. How many are there left?

$$9$$
$$- \; 5$$

Subtracting on a Number Line

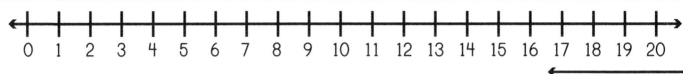

count back

① 6 - 1 = _____

② 9 - 1 = _____

③ 8 - 7 = _____

④ 9 - 3 = _____

⑤ 10 - 2 = _____

⑥ 11 - 1 = _____

⑦ 12 - 4 = _____

⑧ 13 - 5 = _____

⑨ 9 - 7 = _____

⑩ 14 - 9 = _____

⑪ 16 - 6 = _____

⑫ 17 - 4 = _____

⑬ 14 - 8 = _____

⑭ 15 - 3 = _____

⑮ 16 - 4 = _____

⑯ 17 - 7 = _____

⑰ 18 - 9 = _____

⑱ 19 - 5 = _____

⑲ 20 - 5 = _____

Subtraction Word Problems

Read the following statement and subtract the numbers.

1. There are 4  on the street. 2 🐱 go away. How many 🐱 are there left?

$$
\begin{array}{r}
4 \\
- \ 2 \\
\hline

\end{array}
$$

2. Jane has 6 . She ate 3 of them. How many 🍪 does she have left?

$$
\begin{array}{r}
6 \\
- \ 3 \\
\hline

\end{array}
$$

3. Austin has 7 . Ashley took 4 📕 from him. How many 📕 does Austin have left?

$$
\begin{array}{r}
7 \\
- \ 4 \\
\hline

\end{array}
$$

4. There are 9  on tree branch. 5 flew away. How many 🐦 are there left?

$$
\begin{array}{r}
9 \\
- \ 5 \\
\hline

\end{array}
$$

One-digit Subtraction

1) 5
  − 3
  _____

2) 7
  − 2
  _____

3) 3
  − 1
  _____

4) 8
  − 1
  _____

5) 4
  − 2
  _____

6) 4
  − 4
  _____

7) 6
  − 3
  _____

8) 9
  − 2
  _____

9) 7
  − 4
  _____

10) 8
  − 6
  _____

11) 5
  − 4
  _____

12) 6
  − 2
  _____

13) 9
  − 5
  _____

14) 8
  − 4
  _____

15) 8
  − 3
  _____

Color by Subtraction

Subtract the numbers and color each balloon using the color code.

7 - 6

6 - 4

8 - 5

12 - 7

9 - 3

14 - 7

15 - 8

14 - 10

16 - 11

Color Code:

Red = 1

Green = 2

Yellow = 3

Purple = 4

Pink = 5

Orange = 6

Blue = 7

Two-digit Subtraction

Remember to subtract the ones first and then the tens.

1	Tens	Ones
	1	3
-		2

2	Tens	Ones
	1	7
-		2

3	Tens	Ones
	1	4
-		3

4	Tens	Ones
	1	4
-		1

5	Tens	Ones
	1	5
-		2

6	Tens	Ones
	1	4
-		4

7	Tens	Ones
	1	6
-		3

8	Tens	Ones
	1	7
-		3

9	Tens	Ones
	1	5
-		4

10	Tens	Ones
	1	8
-		6

11	Tens	Ones
	1	5
-		4

12	Tens	Ones
	1	6
-		2

13	Tens	Ones
	2	7
-		2

14	Tens	Ones
	2	5
-		4

15	Tens	Ones
	2	9
-		6

Halves

Cross out one circle and count the rest of them.

Cross out two squares and count the rest of them.

Cross out four triangles and count the rest of them.

Cross out five stars and count the rest of them.

Cross out six circles and count the rest of them.

Cross out seven squares and count the rest of them..

Cross out eight triangles and count the rest of them.

Cross out nine stars and count the rest of them.

Cross out ten rectangles and count the rest of them.

Two-digit Subtraction

Remember to subtract the ones first and then the tens.

1
Tens	Ones
1	5
- 1	3

2
Tens	Ones
1	7
- 1	2

3
Tens	Ones
2	3
- 1	1

4
Tens	Ones
1	8
- 1	1

5
Tens	Ones
1	2
- 1	0

6
Tens	Ones
1	4
- 1	3

7
Tens	Ones
1	6
- 1	3

8
Tens	Ones
2	7
- 1	2

9
Tens	Ones
2	7
- 1	4

10
Tens	Ones
2	9
- 1	6

11
Tens	Ones
2	4
- 1	2

12
Tens	Ones
3	6
- 2	5

13
Tens	Ones
3	5
- 1	2

14
Tens	Ones
3	9
- 2	4

15
Tens	Ones
3	8
- 2	3

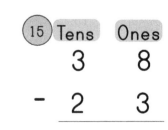

Number Sentences and Number Bonds

Look at the pictures and write number sentences and number bonds.

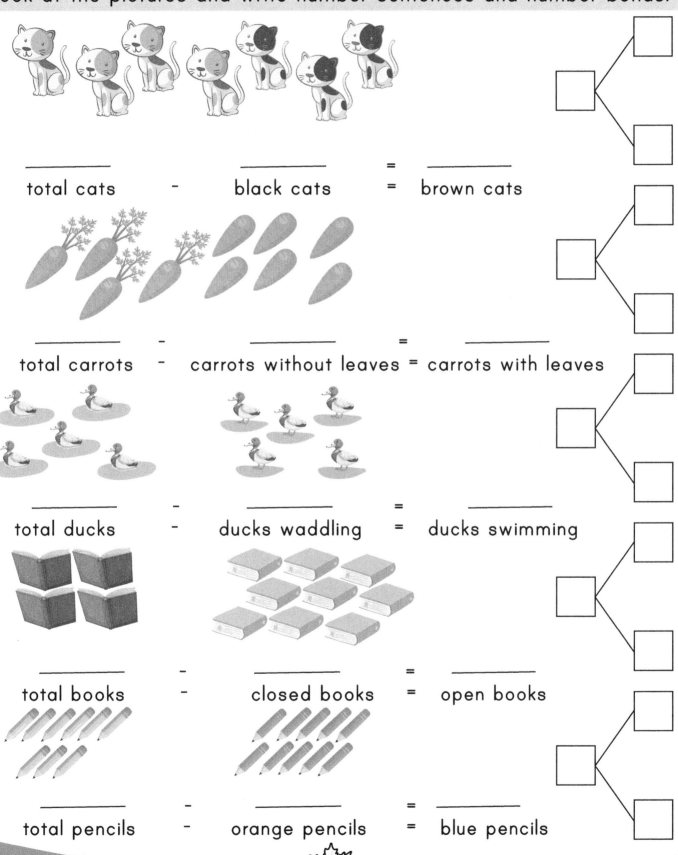

_____   _____   =   _____
total cats   -   black cats   =   brown cats

_____   -   _____   =   _____
total carrots   -   carrots without leaves   =   carrots with leaves

_____   -   _____   =   _____
total ducks   -   ducks waddling   =   ducks swimming

_____   -   _____   =   _____
total books   -   closed books   =   open books

_____   -   _____   =   _____
total pencils   -   orange pencils   =   blue pencils

Two-digit Subtraction (With Borrowing)

Remember to subtract the ones first and then the tens.

1	Tens	Ones
	2	3
−	1	4

2	Tens	Ones
	2	4
−	1	5

3	Tens	Ones
	2	7
−	1	8

4	Tens	Ones
	2	3
−	1	5

5	Tens	Ones
	2	2
−	1	3

6	Tens	Ones
	2	6
−	1	7

7	Tens	Ones
	3	7
−	2	9

8	Tens	Ones
	3	7
−	2	4

9	Tens	Ones
	3	5
−	2	6

10	Tens	Ones
	4	6
−	1	7

11	Tens	Ones
	4	7
−	1	8

12	Tens	Ones
	4	4
−	2	5

68

Relation between Addition and Subtraction

Calculate and solve the missing problems.

1) James bought 5 flowers. He put 3 in one vase and the rest in another vase. How many did he put in the other vase?

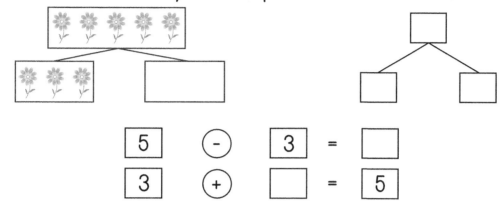

$$5 \; - \; 3 \; = \; \square$$
$$3 \; + \; \square \; = \; 5$$

2) There were 8 kites flying in a garden. 2 of them got caught in trees. How many kites are still flying?

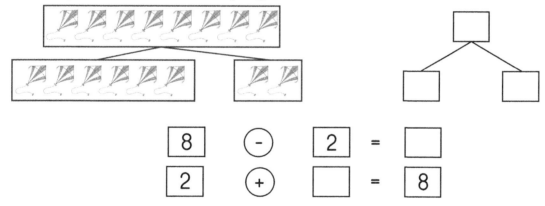

$$8 \; - \; 2 \; = \; \square$$
$$2 \; + \; \square \; = \; 8$$

3) Aina caught 10 fish in two days. She caught 6 in one day. How many did she catch on the other day?

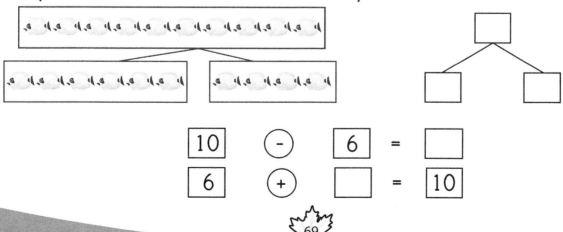

$$10 \; - \; 6 \; = \; \square$$
$$6 \; + \; \square \; = \; 10$$

Calculate the Number

1. How many more does 2 need to make 7?

$$\boxed{7} \;\; \ominus \;\; \boxed{2} \;=\; \boxed{}$$

2. How many more does 5 need to make 9?

$$\boxed{} \;\; \ominus \;\; \boxed{} \;=\; \boxed{}$$

3. How many more does 3 need to make 8?

$$\boxed{} \;\; \ominus \;\; \boxed{} \;=\; \boxed{}$$

4. How many more does 2 need to make 9?

$$\boxed{} \;\; \ominus \;\; \boxed{} \;=\; \boxed{}$$

5. How many more does 4 need to make 10?

$$\boxed{} \;\; \ominus \;\; \boxed{} \;=\; \boxed{}$$

6. How many more does 6 need to make 13?

$$\boxed{} \;\; \ominus \;\; \boxed{} \;=\; \boxed{}$$

7. How many more does 9 need to make 17?

$$\boxed{} \;\; \ominus \;\; \boxed{} \;=\; \boxed{}$$

Subtraction Number Bonds

1 Subtract 2 from 4

4 ⊖ 2 = ☐

1 Subtract 5 from 7

☐ ⊖ ☐ = ☐

1 Subtract 4 from 9

☐ ⊖ ☐ = ☐

1 Subtract 7 from 11

☐ ⊖ ☐ = ☐

1 Subtract 9 from 15

☐ ⊖ ☐ = ☐

Mixed Problems

1	2	3	4	5	6	7	8	9	10
11	12	13	14	15	16	17	18	19	20
21	22	23	24	25	26	27	28	29	30
31	32	33	34	35	36	37	38	39	40
41	42	43	44	45	46	47	48	49	50
51	52	53	54	55	56	57	58	59	60
61	62	63	64	65	66	67	68	69	70
71	72	73	74	75	76	77	78	79	80
81	82	83	84	85	86	87	88	89	90
91	92	93	94	95	96	97	98	99	100

1 more than 18 is		1 less than 25 is	
1 more than 32 is		1 less than 40 is	
1 more than 47 is		1 less than 54 is	
1 more than 64 is		1 less than 61 is	
1 more than 79 is		1 less than 76 is	
1 more than 85 is		1 less than 94 is	

10 more than 8 is		10 less than 15 is	
10 more than 22 is		10 less than 29 is	
10 more than 45 is		10 less than 32 is	
10 more than 63 is		10 less than 53 is	
10 more than 78 is		10 less than 68 is	
10 more than 86 is		10 less than 88 is	

Mixed Problems

12 + 4   23

15 - 3   26

27 - 4   12

9 + 6   31

22 - 5   16

20 + 11   15

39 - 13   17

Solve the following problems.

Add 12 to		Subtract 9 from	
5		13	
9		17	
11		19	
15		21	
20		25	

73

2 Times Table

Learn two times table by counting the number of penguin feet.

 1 penguin ☐ feet = 1 times 2 = 1 x 2 = _____

 2 penguins ☐ feet = 2 times 2 = 2 x 2 = _____

 3 penguins ☐ feet = 3 times 2 = 3 x 2 = _____

 4 penguins ☐ feet = 4 times 2 = 4 x 2 = _____

 5 penguins ☐ feet = 5 times 2 = 5 x 2 = _____

 6 penguins ☐ feet = 6 times 2 = 6 x 2 = _____

7 penguins ☐ feet = 7 times 2 = 7 x 2 = _____

8 penguins ☐ feet = 8 times 2 = 8 x 2 = _____

9 penguins ☐ feet = 9 times 2 = 9 x 2 = _____

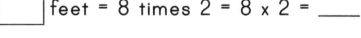 10 penguins ☐ feet = 10 times 2 = 10 x 2 = _____

3 Times Table

 1 tricycle [   ] wheels = 1 times 3 = 1 x 3 = ____

 2 tricycles [   ] wheels = 2 times 3 = 2 x 3 = ____

 3 tricycles [   ] wheels = 3 times 3 = 3 x 3 = ____

 4 tricycles [   ] wheels = 4 times 3 = 4 x 3 = ____

 5 tricycles [   ] wheels = 5 times 3 = 5 x 3 = ____

 6 tricycles [   ] wheels = 6 times 3 = 6 x 3 = ____

 7 tricycles [   ] wheels = 7 times 3 = 7 x 3 = ____

 8 tricycles [   ] wheels = 8 times 3 = 8 x 3 = ____

 9 tricycles [   ] wheels = 9 times 3 = 9 x 3 = ____

 10 tricyles [   ] wheels = 10 times 3 = 10 x 3 = ____

Multiplication

Solve the following operations.

$3 + 3 = $ _____ $ = 3 \times 2 = $ _____

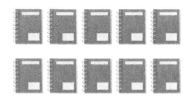

$5 + 5 = $ _____ $ = 5 \times 2 = $ _____

$3 + 3 + 3 + 3 = $ _____ $ = 3 \times 4 = $ _____

$3 + 3 + 3 + 3 + 3 = $ _____ $ = 3 \times 5 = $ _____

$10 + 10 = $ _____ $ = 10 \times 2 = $ _____

NUMBER FRACTIONS

In this chapter, students will learn to:

-Identify equal and unequal parts

- Recognize, find, name, write fractions $\frac{1}{2}$, $\frac{1}{3}$ and $\frac{1}{4}$

of a length, shape, quantity, and set of objects

Equal Parts

Write the number of equal parts in each shape.

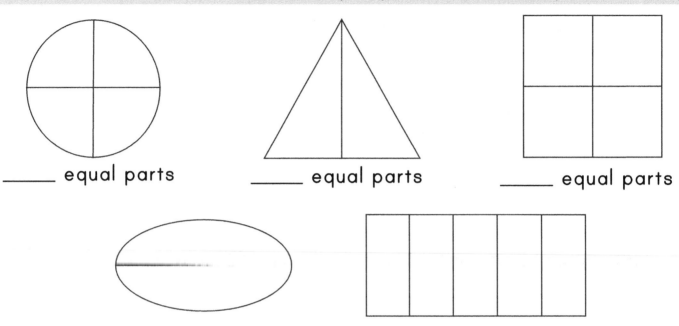

_____ equal parts   _____ equal parts   _____ equal parts

_____ equal parts   _____ equal parts

Color the shape that shows equal parts.

One-Half (1/2)

Draw a straight line on each shape to show halves.

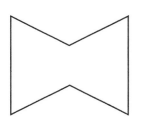  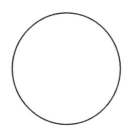 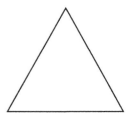

Circle half of the things in each of the following groups.

 1

2

3

4

5

One-Third and One Fourth

How much is shaded? Write $\frac{1}{3}$ or $\frac{1}{4}$ under each line.

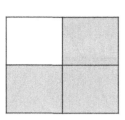 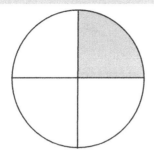 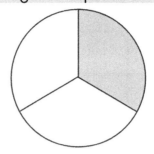 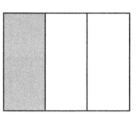

_____   _____   _____   _____

Circle one-third $\frac{1}{3}$ of the things in each of the following groups.

①

②

③

Circle one-foruth $\frac{1}{4}$ of the things in each of the following groups.

①

②

MEASUREMENT

In this chapter, students will learn to:

- Choose and use different non-standard and standard units to measure, calculate, and differentiate length (cm, m) and weight (g, kg).

- Tell time - full hour and half hour

- Tell the time during different activities

- Read the caldendar

Measurement of Length

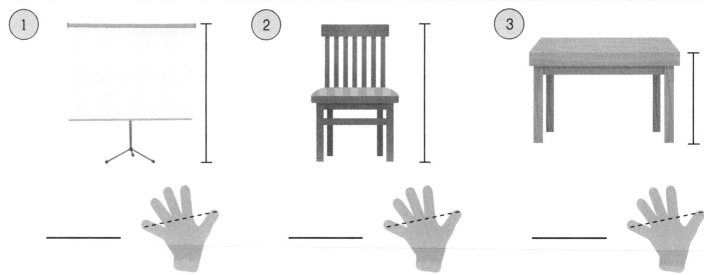

① _____

② _____

③ _____

Measure the lengths of the following things using a centimeter ruler.

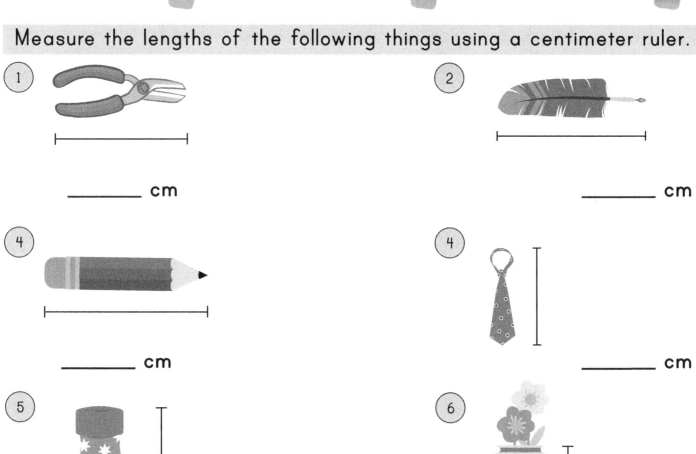

① _____ cm

② _____ cm

④ _____ cm

④ _____ cm

⑤ _____ cm

⑥ _____ cm

Measurement of Weight

(1)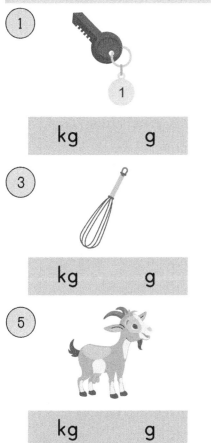

kg   g

(1)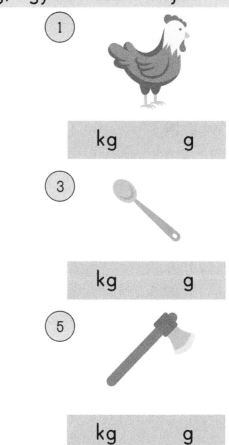

kg   g

(3)

kg   g

(3)

kg   g

(5)

kg   g

(5)

kg   g

Draw lines to match.

lighter than 1 kilogram (kg)

about 1 kilogram (kg)

heavier than 1 kilogram (kg)

Measurement of Capacity

Circle the container that holds more in each group.

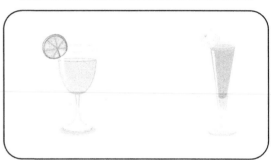

Draw lines to match.

more than 1 liter (l)

about 1 liter (l)

less than 1 liter (l)

more than 1 liter (l)

less than 1 liter (l)

Telling Time - Full Hour

Write the time below each clock.

_____ O' clock

_____ O' clock

_____ O' clock

_____ O' clock

_____ O' clock

_____ O' clock

_____ O' clock

_____ O' clock

_____ O' clock

Telling Time – Half Hour

Write the time below each clock.

_____ O' clock

_____ O' clock

_____ O' clock

_____ O' clock

_____ O' clock

_____ O' clock

_____ O' clock

_____ O' clock

Activity Time

Write the time of each activity that you do by filling in the boxes.

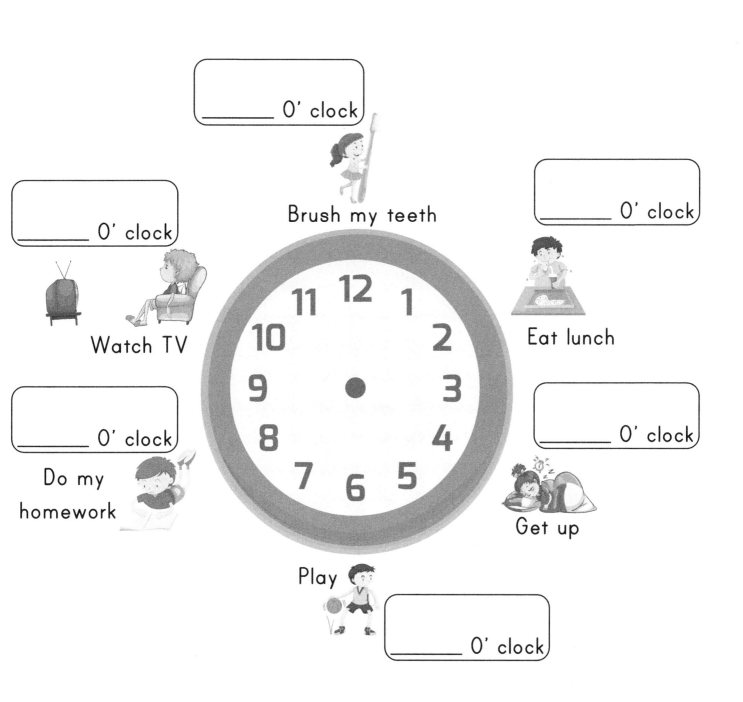

_____ O' clock

Brush my teeth

_____ O' clock

_____ O' clock

Watch TV

Eat lunch

_____ O' clock

Do my homework

_____ O' clock

Get up

Play

_____ O' clock

Calender Reading

Read the calender and answer the following questions.

December 2021						
Sun	Mon	Tue	Wed	Thu	Fri	Sat
			1	2	3	4
5	6	7	8	9	10	11
12	13	14	15	16	17	18
19	20	21	22	23	24	25
26	27	28	29	30	31	

The season is

_____ .

Today's date is

_____/_____/_____

What day will it be on the...

2nd Decemeber _____   10th December _____

15th December _____   21th December _____

25th December _____   31st December _____

What will the date be...

2 days after the 7th of December _____

5 days before the 11th of December _____

2 weeks from the 9th of December _____

What will the day be...

2 days after the 5th of December _____

3 days before the 15th of December _____

1 week from the 11th of December _____

GEOMETRY

In this chapter, students will learn to:

- Describe position and direction

- Draw and measure straight lines

- Identify, name, and recognize shapes.

- Sort and graphically represent shapes

Position and Direction

Color the right hand blue and the left hand green.

Color the arrow indicating the left side red and the right side purple.

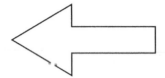 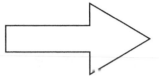

Color the clockwise direction pink and the counterclockwise direction orange

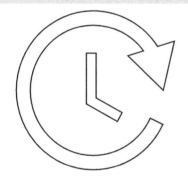 

Write the position of the bird.

   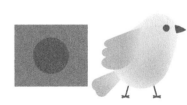

Drawing and Measuring Straight Lines

Measure the length of these straight lines.

1 _____ = _____ cm

2 _____ = _____ cm

3 _____ = _____ cm

4 _____ = _____ cm

Draw straight lines of the following measurement.

1 5 cm

2 6 cm

3 9cm

4 cm

Shape Identification

Color the shapes that have the shape of a circle.

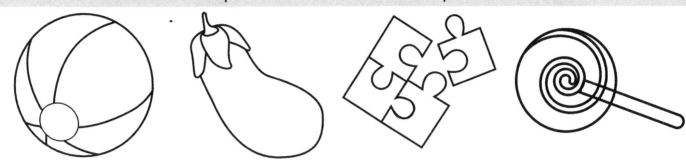

Color the shapes that have the shape of a square.

  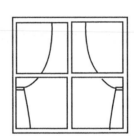 

Color the shapes that have the shape of a triangle.

Color the shapes that have the shape of a rectangle.

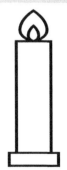   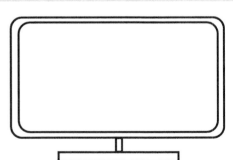

Naming Shapes

Name:_____

Sides: _____

Name:_____

Sides:_____

Name:_____

Sides: _____

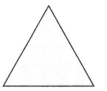

Name:_____

Sides:_____

Name:_____

Sides: _____

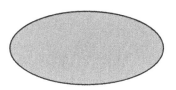

Name:_____

Sides:_____

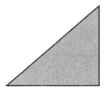

Name:_____

Sides: _____

Name:_____

Sides:_____

Shape Sorting

① ⬤ ⬛ ⬤ ⬛ ⬤ ⬛ _____ _____

① ▭ △ ▭ △ ▭ △ _____ _____

① ★ ⬭ ★ ⬭ ★ ⬭ _____ _____

① ⬤ △ ⬠ ⬤ △ ⬠ ⬤ △ _____ _____

Color the shapes by using the color hint and count each of them.

Color Hint:

△ = _____
⬭ = _____
⬜ = _____
▯ = _____
◯ = _____

Shape Bar Graph

Color the box for each item.

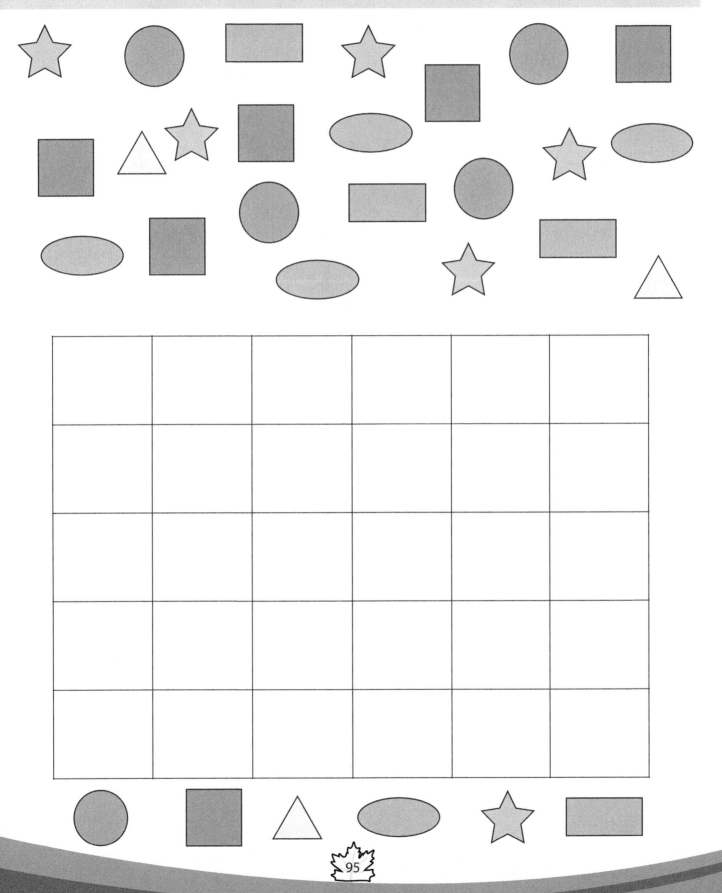

Other books from Brainchild you could find on Amazon

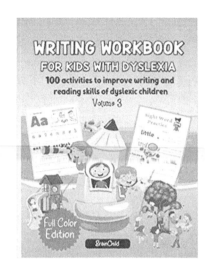

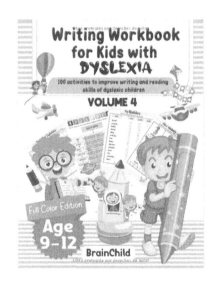

Made in United States
Orlando, FL
14 April 2022

16860043R00057